EASIEST KEYBOARD COLLECTION

Huge Chart Hits

WISE PUBLICATIONS
part of The Music Sales Group
London/New York/Paris/Sydney/Copenhagen/Berlin/Madrid/Tokyo

Published by
Wise Publications

Exclusive Distributors:
Music Sales Limited
14-15 Berners Street,
London W1T 3LJ, UK.
Music Sales Pty Limited
20 Resolution Drive,
Caringbah, NSW 2229, Australia.

Order No. AM1003442
ISBN: 978-1-78038-101-5
This book © Copyright 2011 Wise Publications.

Edited by Jenni Norey.
Music processed by Paul Ewers Music Design.

Printed in the EU.

Your Guarantee of Quality
As publishers, we strive to produce every book to the highest
commercial standards.
Particular care has been given to specifying acid-free, neutral-sized
paper made from pulps which have not been elemental chlorine
bleached. This pulp is from farmed sustainable forests and was
produced with special regard for the environment.
Throughout, the printing and binding have been planned to ensure
a sturdy, attractive publication which should give years of enjoyment.
If your copy fails to meet our high standards, please inform us and
we will gladly replace it.

www.musicsales.com

Contents

THE A TEAM

Words & Music by Ed Sheeran

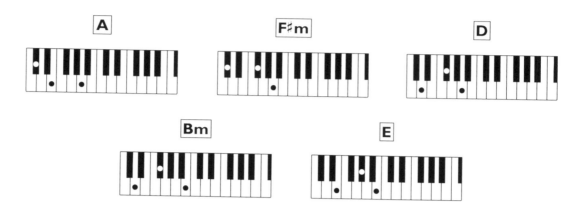

Voice: **Acoustic Guitar**

Rhythm: **Folk**

Tempo: ♩ = 125

White lips,___ pale face,___ breath-ing in___ snow - flakes,___

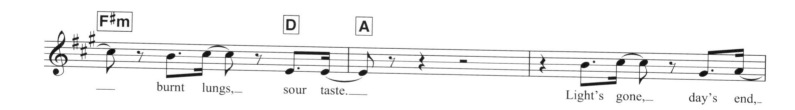

___ burnt lungs,___ sour taste.___ Light's gone,___ day's end,___

___ strug-gl-ing___ to pay___ rent.___ Long nights,___ strange men.___ And

they say___ she's in the Class___ A___ team,___ stuck in her day - dream.__ Been this way_ since

4

eight - een.__ But late - ly__ her face seems_ slow - ly sink - ing,__ wast - ing,__ crum - bl - ing__ like

pas - tries.__ And they__ scream__ the worst things in life come free to us. 'Cause we're

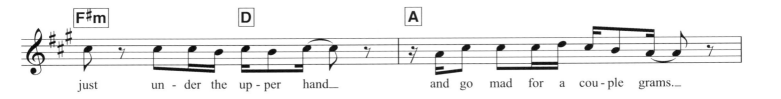

just un - der the up - per hand__ and go mad for a cou - ple grams.__

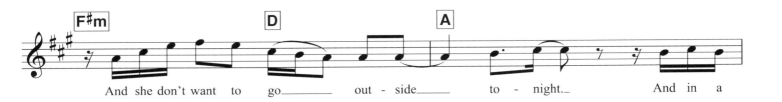

And she don't want to go__ out - side__ to - night.__ And in a

pipe she flies to the Moth - er - land,__ or sells love to an - oth - er man.__

It's too cold__ out - side__ for an - gels to fly,__

an - gels to fly.__

BEST THING I NEVER HAD

Words & Music by Beyoncé Knowles, Kenneth Edmonds, Antonio Dixon, Patrick Smith, Larry Griffin,
Caleb McCampbell & Robert Taylor

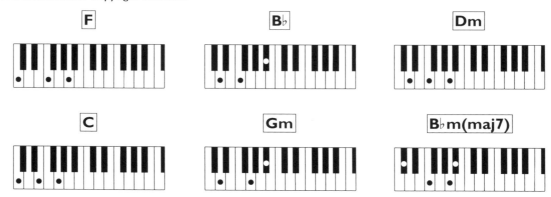

Voice: **Piano & Strings**

Rhythm: **R&B**

Tempo: ♩ = 95

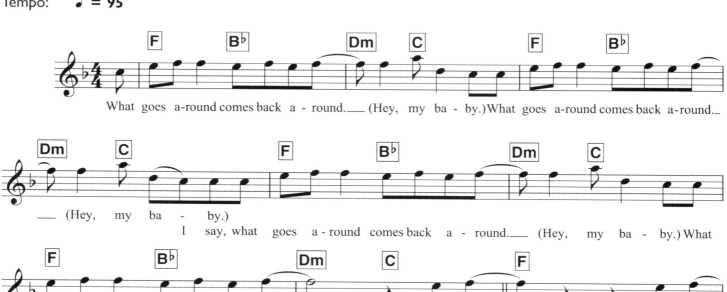

think of the time___ that I al-most loved___ you,___ you showed your ass___ and I,

I saw the re-al you._____ Thank God you blew it. Oh, thank God I dodged the bul-let. I'm so

o-ver you,___ so ba-by good look-in' out._____ I want-ed you bad.___

___ I'm so through with it._____ 'Cause hon-est-ly you___ turned out to be the...___

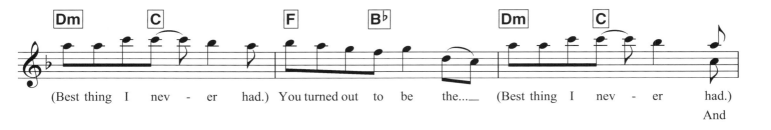

(Best thing I nev-er had.) You turned out to be the...___ (Best thing I nev-er had.) And

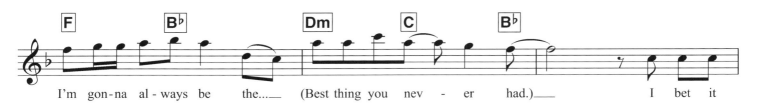

I'm gon-na al-ways be the...___ (Best thing you nev-er had.)___ I bet it

sucks to be you___ right now._____ It sucks to be you___ right now.___

CALIFORNIA KING BED

Words & Music by Jermaine Jackson, Priscilla Hamilton, Andrew Harr & Alexander Delicata

G

Csus2

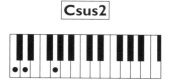

D

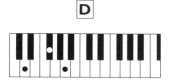

Em

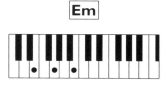

Voice: **Acoustic Guitar**

Rhythm: **16 Beat Rock**

Tempo: ♩ = 95

Chest to chest, ___ nose to nose, ___

palm to palm, ___ we were al - ways just that close.

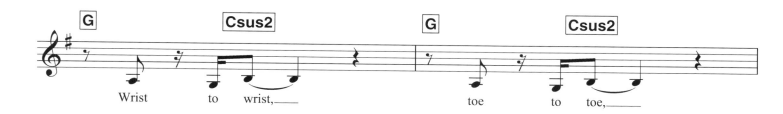

Wrist to wrist, ___ toe to toe, ___

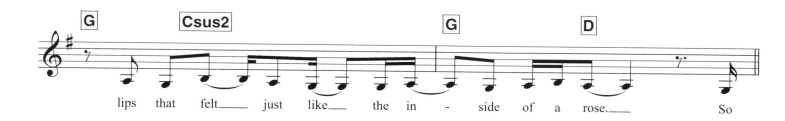

lips that felt ___ just like ___ the in - side of a rose. ___ So

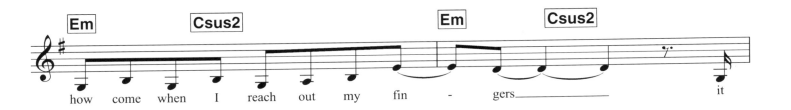

how come when I reach out my fin - gers_____ it

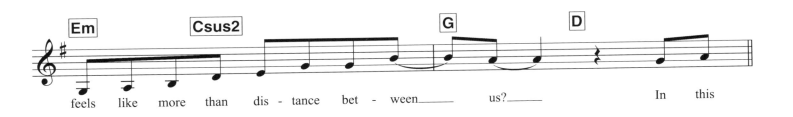

feels like more than dis - tance bet - ween___ us?___ In this

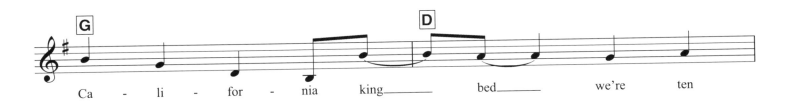

Ca - li - for - nia king___ bed___ we're ten

thou - sand miles a - part.___ I've been Ca - li - for - nia wish-

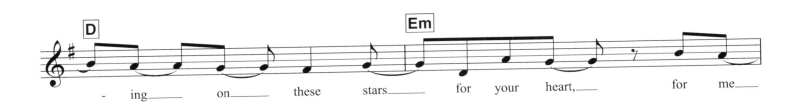

- ing___ on ___ these stars___ for your heart,___ for me___

__ my Ca - li - for - nia king.___

THE EDGE OF GLORY

Words & Music by Fernando Garibay, Stefani Germanotta & Paul Blair

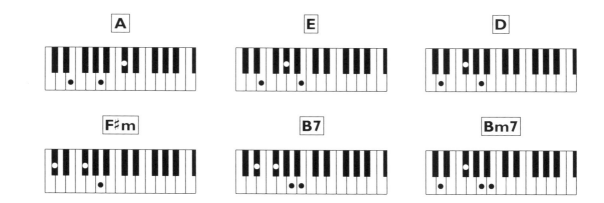

Voice: **Alto Saxophone**

Rhythm: **Disco Pop**

Tempo: ♩ = 130

There ain't a rea-son you and me should be a-lone to-night,_ yeah, ba-by to-night,_ yeah, ba-by.

I got a rea-son that you're who should take me home to-night.__

I need a man_ that thinks it's right when it's so wrong to-night,_ yeah, ba-by to-night,_ yeah, ba-by.

Right on the li-mit's where we know we both be-long to-night.__   It's hot_ to

feel___ the___ rush,___ to brush the dan - ger - rous.___ I'm gon - na

run right to,___ to the edge___ with you, where we can both fall__ far__ in love.___ I'm on the edge___

___ of glo - ry,___ and I'm hang-ing on a mo-ment of truth.___ Out on the edge__

___ of glo - ry,___ and I'm hang-ing on a mo-ment with you.___

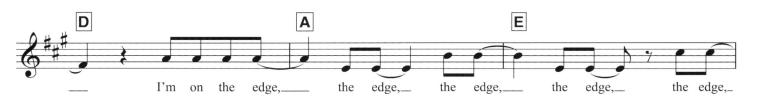

___ I'm on the edge,___ the edge,__ the edge,__ the edge,___ the edge,__

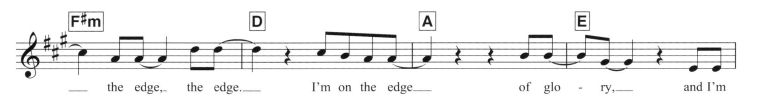

___ the edge,__ the edge.___ I'm on the edge___ of glo - ry,___ and I'm

hang-ing on a mo-ment with you.___ I'm on the edge__ with you.___

ET

Words & Music by Max Martin, Lukasz Gottwald, Joshua Coleman & Katy Perry

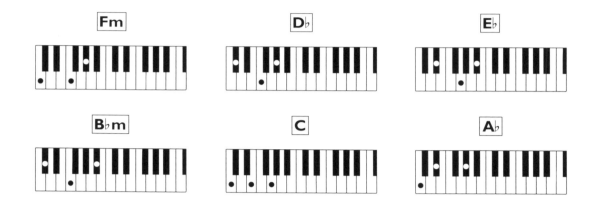

Voice: **Lead Synth**

Rhythm: **Industrial Rock**

Tempo: ♩ = 80

You're so hyp-no-tis-ing could you be the dev-il, could you be an an-gel?

Your touch, mag-net-is-ing, feels like I am float-ing, leave my bod-y glow-ing.

They say be a-fraid you're not like the oth-ers, fu-tur-is-tic lov-er.

Dif-f'rent D. N. A. They don't un-der-stand you. You're from a

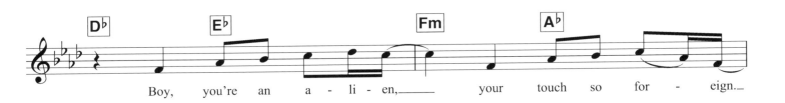

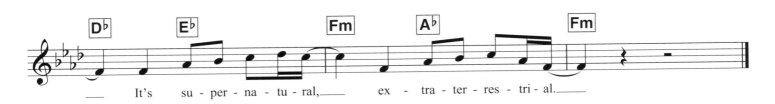

EVERY TEARDROP IS A WATERFALL

Words & Music by Peter Allen, Chris Martin, Brian Eno, Will Champion, Jonny Buckland, Guy Berryman & Adrienne Anderson
© Copyright 2011 Universal Music Publishing MGB Limited.
All rights in Germany administered by Universal Music Publ. GmbH.
All Rights Reserved. International Copyright Secured.

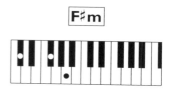

Voice: **Accordion**

Rhythm: **Rock**

Tempo: ♩ = 102

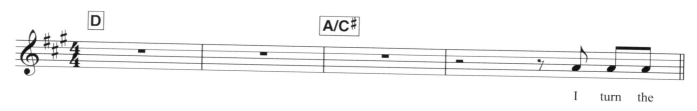

I turn the

mu - sic___ up, I got my re - cords___ on. I shut the

world out - side un - til the lights come_ on. May - be the street's a - light, may - be the

trees are_ gone, but I feel my heart start_ beat - ing to my fav - 'rite_ song. And all the

kids they_ dance, all the kids all_ night. Un - til Mon - day_ morn - ing feels an -

EYES WIDE SHUT

Words & Music by Lars Jensen, Oritsé Williams, Marvin Humes, Jonathan Gill, Aston Merrygold & Tim McEwan

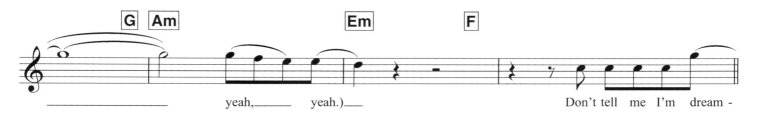

yeah,____ yeah.)___ Don't tell me I'm dream -

- in'____ 'cause if I've been dream - in',____ I, I, I,

I don't ev - er want to wake up. So in love with this feel - in'___ to - night I'll be sleep-

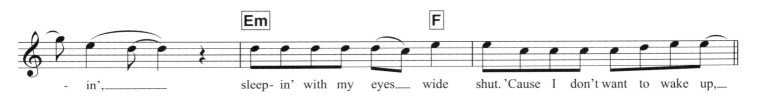

- in',_____ sleep- in' with my eyes___ wide shut. 'Cause I don't want to wake up,__

__ wake up,____ wake up.____ I don't want to wake up,__

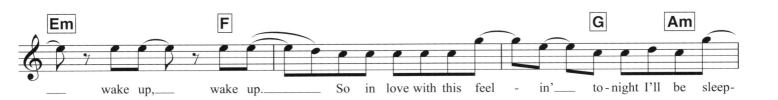

__ wake up,__ wake up.____ So in love with this feel - in'___ to - night I'll be sleep-

- in',_____ sleep- in' with my eyes___ wide shut.

THE FLOOD

Words & Music by Gary Barlow, Howard Donald, Jason Orange, Mark Owen & Robbie Williams

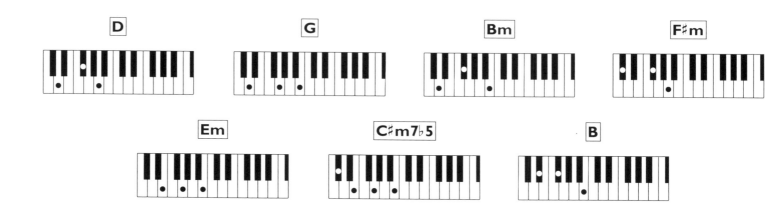

Voice: **Vocal Ah**

Rhythm: **Rock 2**

Tempo: ♩ = 110

Stand - ing   on__ the edge of__ for - ev - er,   at__ the start of__ what-

-ev - er,   shout - ing love at__ the world.

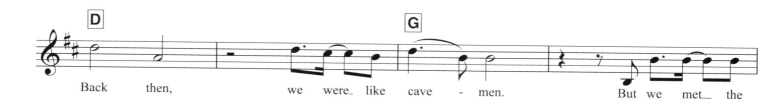

Back   then,   we were_ like cave - men.   But we met__ the

moon and the stars, then we for - gave them.

We will meet you where the lights are. The de - fend - ers of the faith, we are. Where

the thun-der turns a-round they'll run so hard we'll tear the ground a - way. You know

no one dies, in these love - drowned eyes. Through our

love - drowned eyes we'll watch you sleep to - night.

Al - though no one un-der-stood, we were hold-ing back the flood, learn-ing how to dance the

rain. We were hold-ing back the flood. They said we'd nev-er dance a - gain.

FOOLIN'

Words & Music by Dionne Bromfield & Francis Eg White

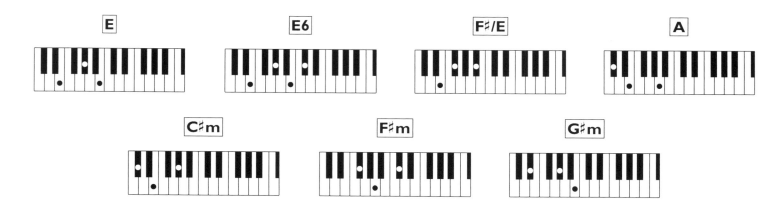

Voice: **Alto Saxophone**

Rhythm: **Funk Rock**

Tempo: ♩ = 120

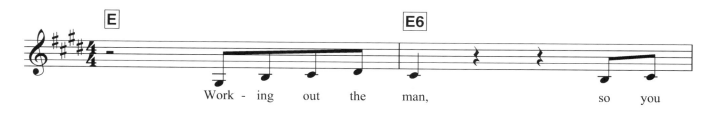

Work - ing out the man, so you

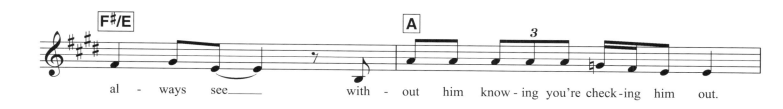

al - ways see____ with - out him know - ing you're check-ing him out.

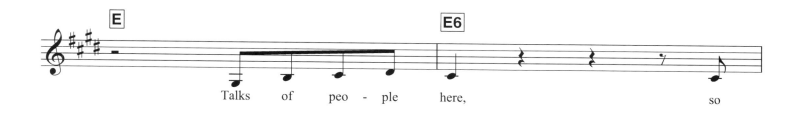

Talks of peo - ple here, so

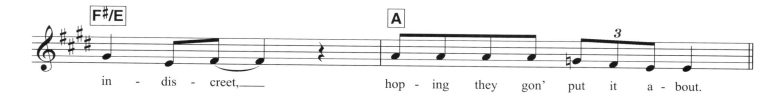

in - dis - creet,____ hop - ing they gon' put it a - bout.

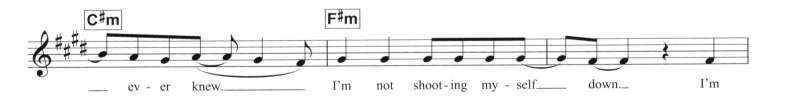

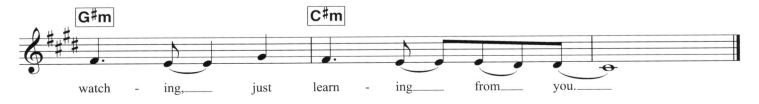

FORGET YOU

Words & Music by Thomas Callaway, Philip Lawrence, Peter Hernandez, Ari Levine & Christopher Brown

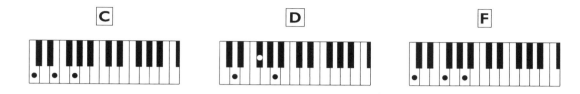

Voice: **Electric Guitar**

Rhythm: **Funk Rock**

Tempo: ♩ = 130

I see you driv-ing 'round town with the girl I love___ and I'm like,___

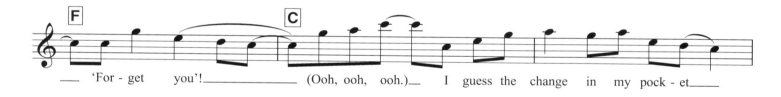

___ 'For-get you'!_____ (Ooh, ooh, ooh.)___ I guess the change in my pock-et___

was-n't e-nough.___ I'm like,___ 'For-get you! And for-get her too'. I said,

if I was rich-er,___ I'd still be with___ ya.___ Ha, now ain't that some...

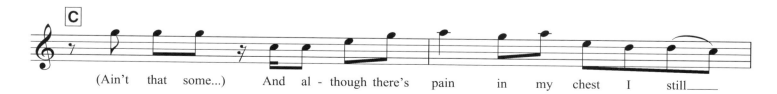

(Ain't that some...) And al-though there's pain in my chest I still___

wish you the best___ with her. For-get you!___ (Ooh, ooh, ooh.)___ Yeah, I'm

sor - ry, I can't af-ford a Fer-ra-ri, but

that don't mean I can't get you there.___ I guess he's an

X - box and I'm more like A-ta-ri. Mm, but the

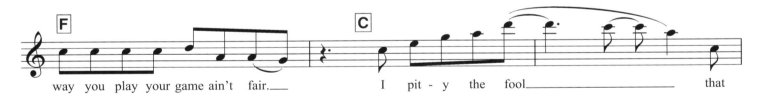
way you play your game ain't fair.___ I pit-y the fool___ that

falls in love with you,___ oh. (Oh, she's a gold dig-ger.) Well... (Just thought you should know...)

Ooh.___ I've got some news for you:

DON'T HOLD YOUR BREATH

Words & Music by Billy Steinberg, Joshua Berman & Tobias Gad

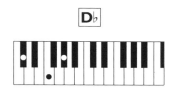
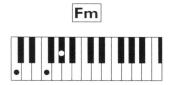
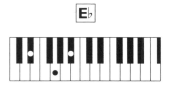

Voice: **Flute**

Rhythm: **Disco Pop**

Tempo: ♩ = 125

You can't touch me now, there's no_____ feel - ing left. If you

think I'm com - ing back,____ don't____ hold your breath.____

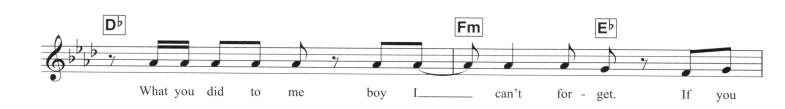

What you did to me boy I____ can't for - get. If you

think I'm com - ing back,____ don't____ hold your breath, eh, eh.____

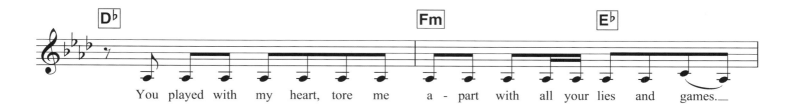

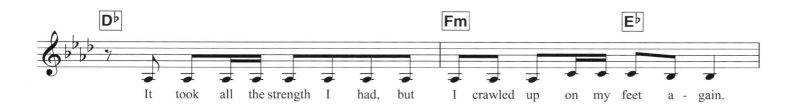

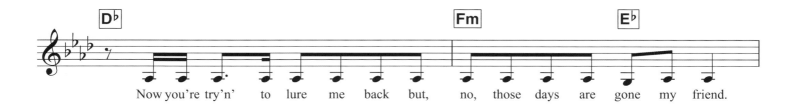

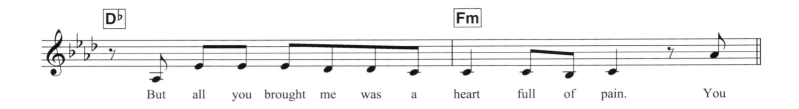

But all you brought me was a heart full of pain. You

can't touch me now, there's no_____ feel - ing left. If you

think I'm com - ing back,____ don't_____ hold your breath.____

What you did to me, boy, I_____ can't for - get. If you

think I'm com - ing back,____ don't____ hold your breath, eh, eh.____

GOOD GIRL

Words & Music by Mikkel Eriksen, Tor Erik Hermansen, Sandy Wilhelm & Autumn Rowe

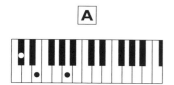
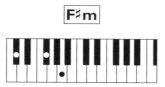
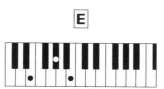
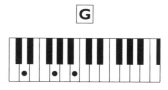

Voice: **Synth Lead**

Rhythm: **Dance Pop**

Tempo: ♩ = 135

I like tight jeans, dark shades. When I walk the ground shakes (Boom.) like an eight-o-eight.

(Boom.) You ap-pre-ci-ate my lean bod-y, nice shape. Wan-na take me on a date?

(Move.) You've got what it takes. (Move.) You bet-ter have some cake. I like___ how I'm

catch-ing your eye.___ I, I, I, I like___ how I don't e-ven try.___ I, I, I,

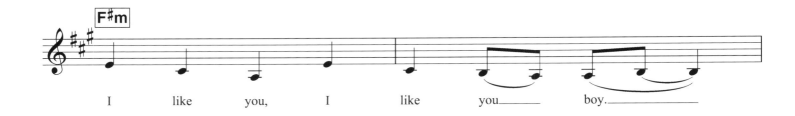

I like you, I like you____ boy.____

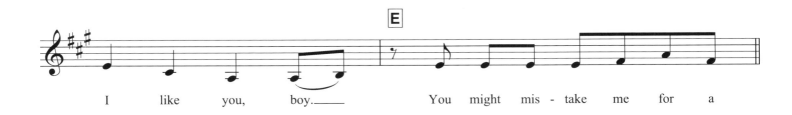

I like you, boy.____ You might mis - take me for a

heart____ break - er____ 'cause there's blood on the floor.____ I'm

hop - ing you____ will see, there's some-thing good____ in me ne - ver seen be - fore.____

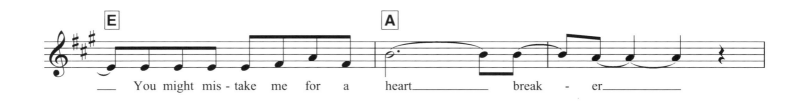

____ You might mis - take me for a heart____ break - er____

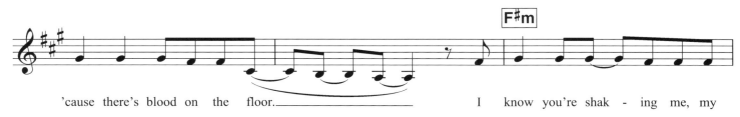

'cause there's blood on the floor.____ I know you're shak - ing me, my

heart is there____ for keeps, there's an o - pen door.____ I know I can be a

good, good girl.____ I know I can be a good, good girl.____

I know I can be a good girl. But I've been bad be - fore.____

Good girl... I know I can be a good, good girl.____

I know I can be a good, good girl.____ I know I can be a

good girl. But I've been bad be - fore.____ Good girl, but I've been bad be - fore.____

JUST THE WAY YOU ARE

Words & Music by Ari Levine, Bruno Mars, Philip Lawrence, Peter Hernandez, Khari Cain & Khalil Walton

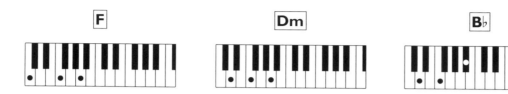

Voice: **Piano**

Rhythm: **Folk Rock**

Tempo: ♩ = 115

Her eyes, her eyes__ make the stars look__ like they're not shin-ing.

Her hair, her hair falls per-fect-ly__ with-out her try-ing.

She's so beau-ti-ful__ and I tell her ev-'ry__

__ day.__ Yeah,__ I know, I know__ when I

com-pli-ment__ her she won't be-lieve me. And it's so, it's so__ sad to

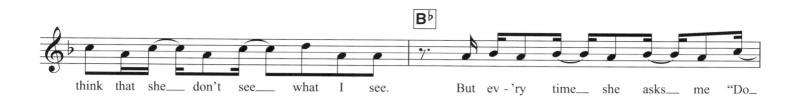
think that she_ don't see_ what I see. But ev-'ry time_ she asks_ me "Do_

_ I look_ o - kay?" I say:_ When I see your face,_

_ there's not a thing_ that I_ would change_

_ 'cause you're a - maz - ing_ just_ the way_ you are._

And when you smile,_ the whole world stops_

_ and stares_ for a while._ 'Cause girl you're a - maz - ing_ just_

_ the way_ you are._ Yeah._

31

L.I.F.E.G.O.E.S.O.N.

Words & Music by Charlie Fink

E
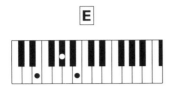

A
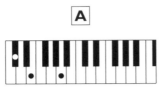

F♯m
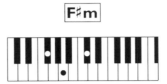

B
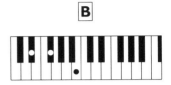

Voice: **Electric Guitar**

Rhythm: **16 Beat Rock**

Tempo: ♩ = 90

Li - sa likes bran - dy and the way it hits her lips. She's a

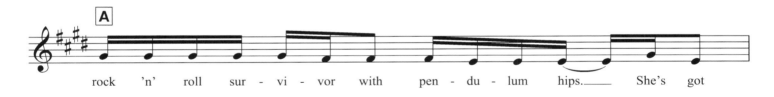

rock 'n' roll sur - vi - vor with pen - du - lum hips.___ She's got

deep brown eyes___ that have seen it all.

Work - ing at a night - club that was called The A - ven - ue. The bar___

___ men used to call her 'Lit - tle Li - sa, Loon - ey Tunes'. She went

PRICE TAG

Words & Music by Lukasz Gottwald, Claude Kelly, Bobby Ray Simmons & Jessica Cornish

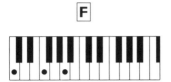

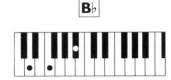

Voice: **Electric Guitar**

Rhythm: **Swing Rock**

Tempo: ♩ = 86

Seems like ev-'ry-bod-y's got a price,___ I won-der how they sleep at

night. When the sale comes first, and the truth comes se-cond, just stop for a min-ute and

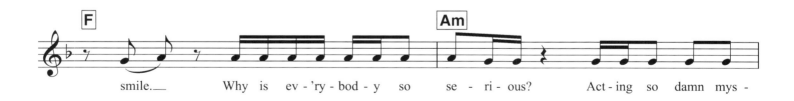

smile.___ Why is ev-'ry-bod-y so se-ri-ous? Act-ing so damn mys-

-ter-i-ous,___ got shades on your eyes and your heels so high that you can't e-ven have a good

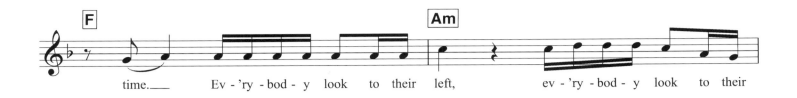

time.__ Ev-'ry-bod-y look to their left, ev-'ry-bod-y look to their

right. Can you feel that, yeah, we're pay-ing with love to - night._ It's not a - bout the

mon-ey, mon-ey, mon-ey._ We don't need your mon-ey, mon-ey, mon-ey._ We just wan-na make the

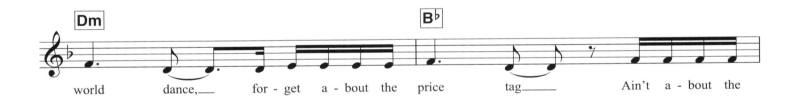

world dance,_ for - get a - bout the price tag___ Ain't a - bout the

(Uh.) cha - ching,_ cha - ching. Ain't a - bout the (Yeah.) ba - bling,_ ba - bling. Wan-na make the

world dance,_ for - get a - bout the price tag.__

SHE SAID

Words & Music by Benjamin Drew, Eric Appapoulay, Richard Cassell & Tom Goss

Dm 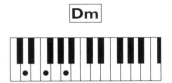 **A** 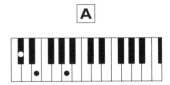 **F**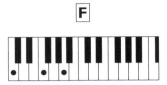

Voice: **Flute**

Rhythm: **Swing**

Tempo: ♩ = 130

She said "I love you boy, I love you so."____ She said "I love you ba - by,

oh, oh, oh, oh,____ oh."____

She said "I love you more than words can say."____ She said "I love you ba -

-a - a - a - a - a - by."____

So I said___ "What you're say-ing girl, it can't be right.___

How can you be in love with me?__ We on-ly just met to-night."_____

So she said___ "Boy I loved you from the start,_____

when I first heard 'Love Goes Down',__ some-thing start-ed burn-ing in my heart."_____

I said "Stop___ this cra-zy talk___

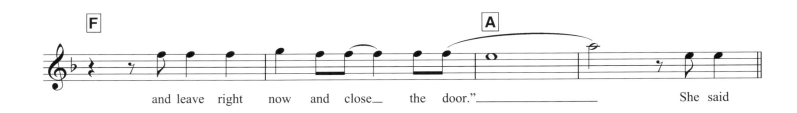

and leave right now and close the door." She said

"But I love you boy, I love you so." She said "I love you ba - by,

oh, oh, oh, oh, oh."

She said "I love you more than words can say." She said "I love you ba -

-a - a - a - a - by."

SOMEONE LIKE YOU

Words & Music by Adele Adkins & Daniel Wilson

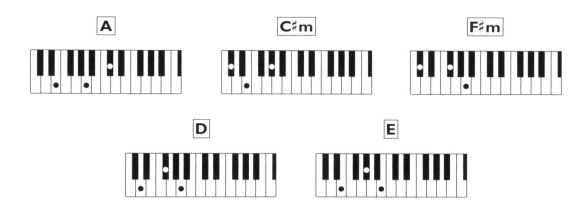

Voice: **Piano**

Rhythm: **Blues Rock**

Tempo: ♩ = 75

I_____ heard_____ that you're set-tled down, that you

found a girl___ and you're mar-ried now._____ I heard that your

dreams came true. Guess she gave you things_ I did-n't give to you.___

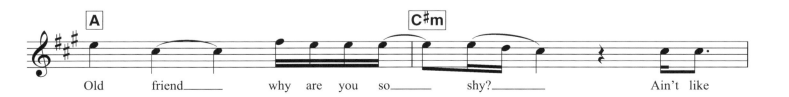

Old friend_____ why are you so_____ shy?_____ Ain't like

you to hold___ back or___ hide from the light._____ I

hate to turn up_____ out of the blue un - in - vi - ted, but I_____

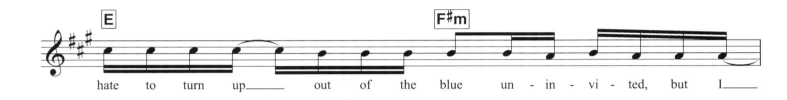

___ could - n't stay a - way_____ I could - n't fight it. I had

hoped you'd see my face and that you'd be re - min - ded that for

me it is - n't o - ver._____

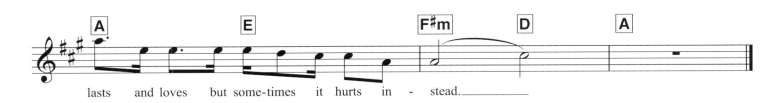

SKINNY LOVE

Words & Music by Justin Vernon
© Copyright 2008 April Base Publishing, USA.
Chrysalis Music Limited.
All Rights Reserved. International Copyright Secured.

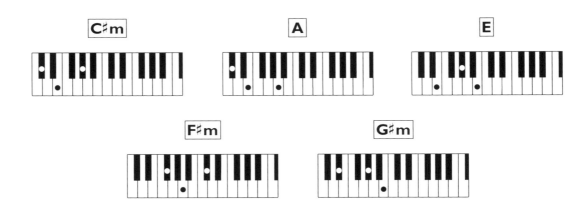

Voice: **Piano**

Rhythm: **Ballad**

Tempo: ♩ = 70

Come on skin-ny love___ just last the year.___

Pour a lit-tle salt___ we were nev-er here.___ My my my,___

___ my my my,___ my my my___ my my...___ Star - ing at the

sink of blood and crushed_ ve - neer.___

Tell my love___ to wreck it all.___

Cut out all___ the ropes and let me fall._____ My my my,___

___ my my my,___ my my my___ my my... Right___ in the mo-

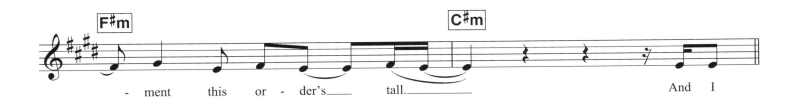

- ment this or-der's___ tall._____ And I

told you to___ be pa-tient and I told you to___ be fine.___ And I

told you to___ be bal-anced and I told you to___ be kind._ And in the

morn-ing I'll___ be with___ you. But it will be a dif-f'rent kind._ 'Cause I'll be

hold-ing all___ the tick-ets and you'll be own-ing all___ the fines._

SUN OF A GUN

Words & Music by Harry James & Nanna Fabricius

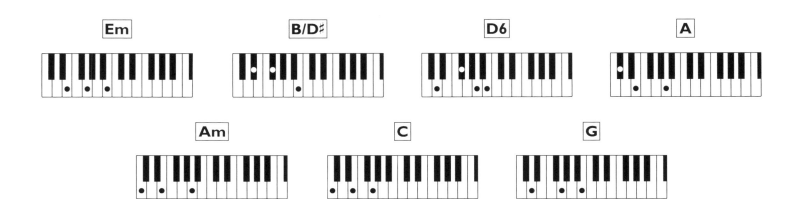

Voice: **Flute**

Rhythm: **Pop**

Tempo: ♩ = 135

(Ooh, ooh, ooh, ooh, ooh, ooh, ooh, ooh, ooh,

ooh, ooh, ooh, ooh, ooh, ooh, ooh, ooh.)

Once burned, twice shy, too much of your light made me blind.

I'd wait all night, but you left one too man-y times.

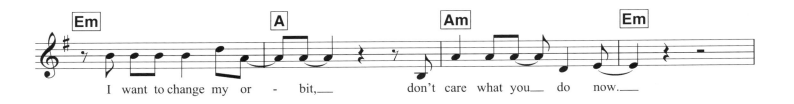

I want to change my or - bit,___ don't care what you___ do now.___

I want to live in dark - ness,___ don't want to be spun a - round.___

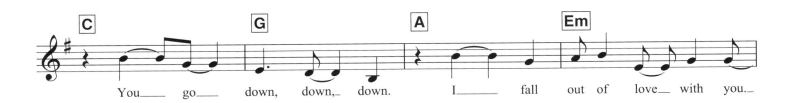

You___ go___ down, down,___ down. I___ fall out of love___ with you.___

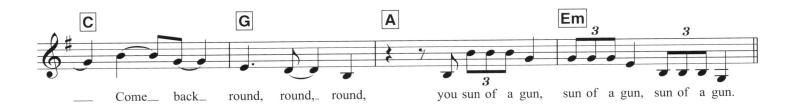

___ Come___ back___ round, round,___ round, you sun of a gun, sun of a gun, sun of a gun.

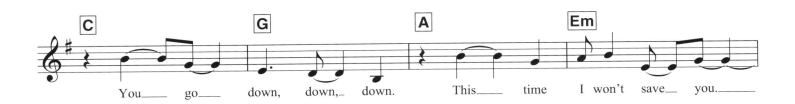

You___ go___ down, down,___ down. This___ time I won't save___ you.___

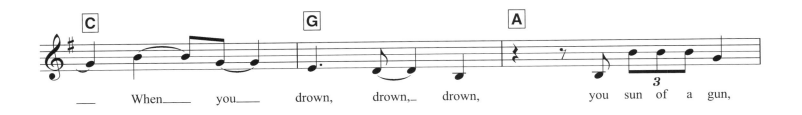

___ When___ you___ drown, drown,___ drown, you sun of a gun,

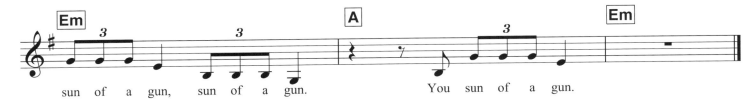

sun of a gun, sun of a gun. You sun of a gun.

YOUR SONG

Words & Music by Elton John & Bernie Taupin

© Copyright 1969 Dick James Music Limited.
Universal/Dick James Music Limited.
All rights in Germany administered by Universal Music Publ. GmbH.
All Rights Reserved. International Copyright Secured.

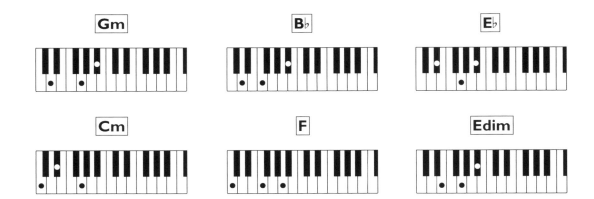

Voice: **Piano**

Rhythm: **Slow Rock**

Tempo: ♩ = 135

It's a lit-tle bit fun-ny,___ this feel-ing in - side.___

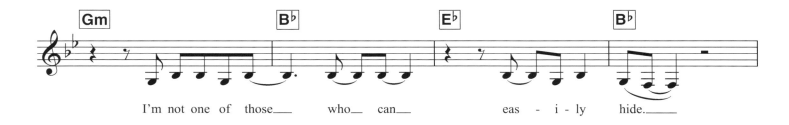

I'm not one of those___ who__ can___ eas - i - ly hide.___

I don't have_ much mon - ey,___ but boy, if I did

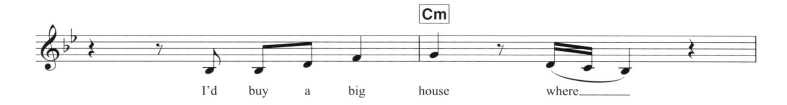

I'd buy a big house where___

we both   could live.

So ex - cuse me for - get - ting,   but these things I do.

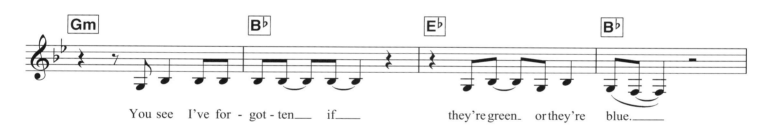

You see I've for - got - ten   if   they're green   or they're blue.

An - y - way the thing is,   what I real - ly

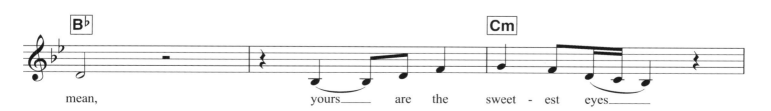

mean,   yours   are the sweet - est eyes

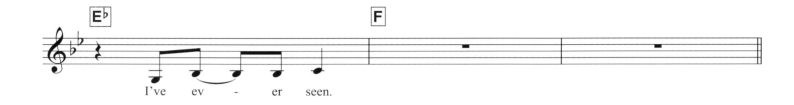

I've ev - er seen.

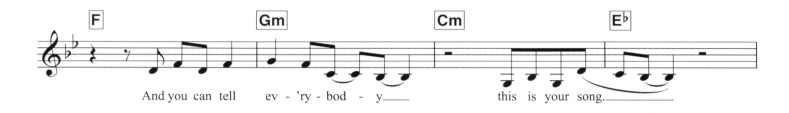

And you can tell ev - 'ry - bod - y____ this is your song.____

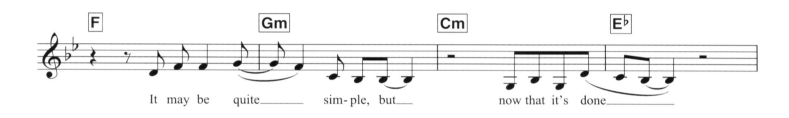

It may be quite____ sim - ple, but____ now that it's done____

I hope you don't mind,____ I hope you don't mind____ that I put down in

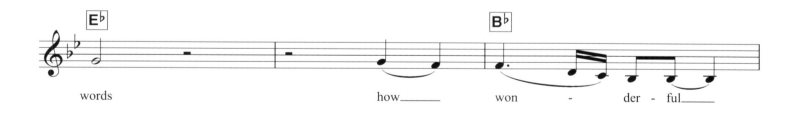

words how____ won - der - ful____

life is____ now you're____ in the____ world.____